Sto ✓

The Tale of the

WHITEFOOT MOUSE

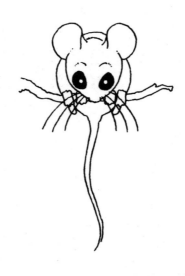

WILD WORLD TALES

THE
Tale of the
WHITEFOOT
MOUSE

by

H E N R Y   B .   K A N E

ALFRED · A · KNOPF

New York

Distributed simultaneously in Canada by Random House of Canada,
Limited, Toronto.

T O

B E T T Y   J A N E

who, as the wife and mother of naturalists,

has ceased to be surprised

at anything.

The Tale of the

WHITEFOOT MOUSE

A robin storm of early April
had left the earth covered with a deep white blanket
of snow. It was already melting under the warmth of
a gentle spring breeze before the morning sun awoke.

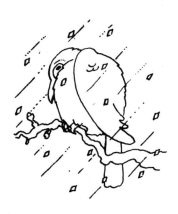

$\mathcal{H}$ere and there winding lines of little tracks ran over open spaces and under juniper bushes. They were the tracks of the white-footed mice who had spent the night playing over the surface of the newly fallen snow, their tails leaving long marks at every leap.

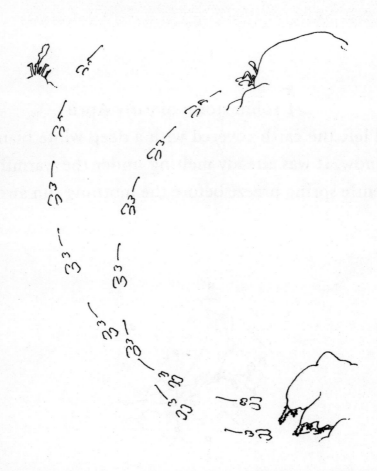

One of these trails led to an old wall and disappeared beneath its snow-covered stones. Down and down it went into the ground through a long winding tunnel. Here, safe from wind and snow, lived a family of whitefeet. The little babies' eyes were closed tight and their tiny ears were folded close to their heads. They were less than a day old.

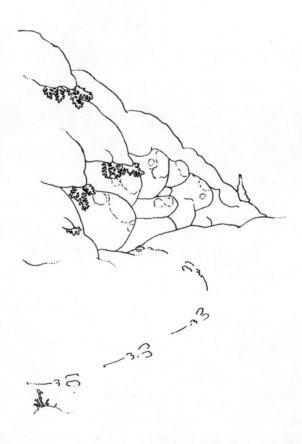

In the days that followed, the snow disappeared and the furry buds of the hepatica unfolded and lifted their light-blue blossoms to the sun.

Within a week the little mice were covered with a coat of short gray fur. They were always hungry and they grew fast. But one grew faster and stronger than all the rest. At dinner he was always first; in their tumbling and rolling he was always on top.

One night when his mother had left the nest he started out alone. Up the tunnel he went, stumbling and falling at every step. Finally he came to the great world outside. The moss beneath his feet was damp, the night smells that came to his little nose were strange and new. And then his courage left him and the air was filled with his frightened little squeaks.

On a log near by sat his mother nibbling a hasty lunch. Suddenly she sat up and listened as the cries of her young son came to her ears. Then she was off like a flash, over moss and leaves and purple violets. At the entrance to the nest she found him—and none too soon, for as she picked him up in her teeth and hustled him inside, two fierce black eyes looked down from the top of the wall.

The weasel had arrived just too late, and as he snarled and turned away, the little mouse, safe again at home, settled happily down to dinner.

*T*wo weeks after their birth the mice opened their eyes for the first time. Although it was dark in the nest they didn't mind. Their eyes were meant for seeing in the dark. A week later their mother brought them seeds from the storehouse and they soon learned to eat these in place of milk.

It was dusk of a warm day in May, just a month after the big snow, when they came to the tunnel's mouth together for the first time. By now they were almost two-thirds grown. Their fur was soft and gray above, while underneath it was as white as that same snow.

Each day they had been exploring farther and farther up the tunnel and now, at last, they stole outside. Huddled together, their long whiskers twitching nervously, through their coal-black eyes and big round ears they took in every sight and sound in this strange new world above the ground.

Two nights later they left home.

June came. At the upper end of the pasture an old apple tree leaned against the wall. In it the little whitefoot had found a home. Here he felt safe as he slept away the daylight hours.

At night he scrambled down the sloping trunk onto the grape vine that reached up from the stone wall, and off he went through the ferns and the juniper.

One sunny afternoon a frightful noise awoke him from his sound sleep. His long white whiskers quivered with fear as a black shadow fell across his doorway and again came that terrifying sound.

Hardly knowing what he did, the little mouse flashed out the door, leaped to the ground, and raced off through the grass to the protection of a clump of weeds.

Behind him a hungry young crow cawed once more for his dinner.

Shivering with dread, the frightened youngster hid beneath the overhanging leaves, safe for the moment. But not for long. Greedy eyes had seen his hurried flight. A huge blacksnake slid slowly across the grass, his head held high, his unwinking eyes searching every possible hiding-place. The young mouse saw him coming. Instinct told him that here was something from which he must escape.

*W*ith a bound he left his shelter and once more was off across the pasture. Behind him raced the black-snake. With alarming speed the distance between them grew less and less until it seemed that he must be overtaken.

But suddenly he saw before him an unexpected haven of safety, an old barn. With almost his last gasp he reached it and leaped up its side to a welcome hole. Hanging there for a moment, he regained his breath, then popped into the gloom of the haymow. Outside, the defeated snake slid off into the long grass to search for less lively prey.

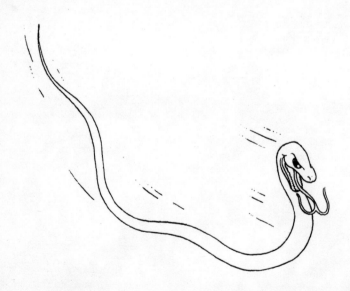

*F*or long minutes the young whitefoot shivered in the half-light. But soon his frightening experience was forgotten and he started off on a tour of this huge new cave. Sunlight streamed through holes in its sides and roof, and the summer breeze blew gently through windows that had long since lost their panes. He scampered across a beam, peering over its edge at the hay-covered floor far below. At the far end great gaps showed under the eaves.

He soon discovered his approach was being watched by eight shiny eyes peeking over the top of a mound of moss and grass. Slowly, very slowly, he crept closer while the fledgling phoebes shrank lower into their nest.

Then from the roof outside came the sharp clear call of their mother: "Fe-bee, Fe-bee," and a moment later with a rush of wings she swooped in under the eaves. The little mouse hastened away.

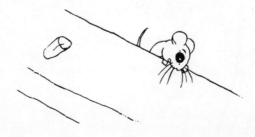

But his greatest surprise was still to come. At the far end of the barn he spied two little balls of fur pressed close against the rough wall. He moved cautiously forward. Then one of the balls came to life and a sharp beady eye peeked out over a fold of dark-brown skin. Puzzled, the mouse sat up and with a front paw drummed noisily on the beam. The little brown bats awoke with a start. They unfolded their wings, half spread them at their sides, and hitched away while black pin-head eyes glared from under huge ears and from their mouths came defiant squeaks and hisses.

The mouse edged closer, then shrank back as great wings unfolded and together the bats fluttered off. He watched them as they wheeled round and round, then saw them disappear from sight in a crack high up above him.

*A*t last his wanderings led him down to the floor of the barn. Wide cracks and broken boards showed that it was seldom used. It was littered with chaff, among other seeds many from his favorite clover. Occasionally he came across a well-filled head of wild oats, soft and full of a milky juice that quenched his thirst.

He ate and ate and ate until it seemed as though he would burst, then set out to search for a safe spot in which to continue his interrupted sleep. Under an old buggy he found a ball of cotton padding, pulled from the seat-back by another mouse before him. The sleepy wanderer crawled inside, pushed back the sagging walls, and, curling up comfortably, fell into a dreamless sleep.

Summer passed and in its place came the sharp frosty nights of autumn. No longer was he a little mouse, but a full-grown whitefoot. His soft furry coat had changed from gray to warm brown above, while his feet and under parts were still the same snowy white of his younger days.

The summer nights had been spent playing on the floor of the pine woods and across the open pasture with others of his kind. One in particular he found who took more pleasure in his company than any of the rest. When fall came she went with him to the alder swamp and in an old catbird's nest they built themselves a home. They covered it with leaves and grass and grape bark, and lined it with the fluffy white clouds of the milkweed.

Neither the whitefoot nor his mate had ever seen winter. Yet something, long before the need arose, told them just what to do.

When the winds and the frosts sent the weed seeds flying, opened the shells of the shagbark and the burs of the beech, the two scurried about gathering their winter's supply. They went to the upper pasture, the hardwood ridge, and the swamp meadow, returning with their cheek pouches bulging like toy balloons. In a hole beneath an old stump they stored it.

But even now life was not all work. At night they found time to race over the fallen leaves and to play tag up and down the skeleton branches of the alders.

One night, under a chill October moon, they were playing over and around their nest when suddenly they stopped, every nerve tense, every whisker quivering. From overhead came that fearful, dreaded cry:

"*H*oo ho hoo-hooo, Hoo ho hoo-hoooo." And then a huge black shape blotted out the moon.

The two mice leaped wildly into mid-air not a moment too soon, for behind them the hoot owl, on silent wings, hit the nest with the force of an explosion, scattering it to the four winds. Before he could recover himself, his hoped-for victims were far away, racing across the swamp bottom under the welcome cover of the overhanging marsh grass.

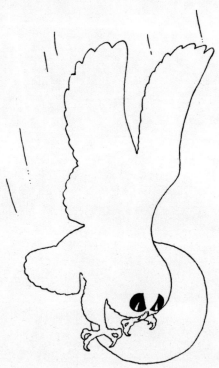

The whitefeet wasted no time in regrets, but the next morning they set about looking for a new home. Beneath an old log they found a hole, half covered with fallen leaves. They stole in to investigate. But their noses told them it was occupied, that a chipmunk was at home, already starting his winter's sleep.

An inviting hole showed in the side of a weather-beaten old chestnut. Here again they found they were too late. A pair of flying squirrels were sound asleep inside, curled in a soft furry ball with their tails wrapped tightly about them.

But at last they were successful. They found a deserted chickadee's nest in the hollow limb of an apple tree and it became their new home.

The apple tree was far removed from the food supply which they had so carefully hidden under the old stump. Their earlier work was wasted, but they soon set about gathering another store. Nuts were not to be had so easily now. The gray and red squirrels, the chipmunks, and the other whitefeet had not been idle. Seeds, however, were still to be found, and before long a new supply was laid away.

And so at the end of the year the two whitefeet were carefree and happy. Occasionally an inquisitive chickadee stopped to peek in at their doorway and sing them a cheery song. Through the short days when the icy winds roared down from the north, when the sleet drove through the bare branches, and the snow swirled into every nook and corner, they slept snug and warm in their cozy nest.

*B*ut at night, when the trees snapped and crackled with the cold, two tiny figures raced across the glittering forest floor.

And sometimes through the midnight woods came a sound that seemed like the sweet distant singing of a bird. The cold pale moon shone down on a snow-laden bough where the little whitefoot sat, singing his happy far-away song, a song that seemed to say, no matter what the weather, in his heart it was always spring.

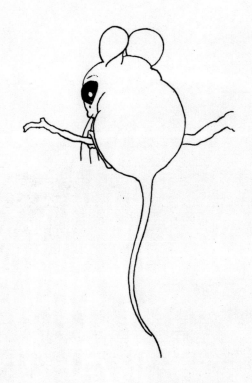